# I-SPY

# BUTTERFLIES AND MOTHS

*This book belongs to:*

_____

_____

**Swallowtail**
This is the largest European butterfly. In Britain you will find it only in a few East Anglian wetlands. On holiday in France you will probably see lots of them.
*I-Spy for* **50**

**Small Tortoiseshell**
You will easily see this butterfly in your garden, especially if you have some of its favourite flowers, such as buddleia, ice-plant, or Michaelmas daisy. It may even come into your house in autumn. Why do you think it does this?

*I-Spy for* **5**
*Double with answer*

## Peacock

The bright-blue, eye-like markings on the wings make this the most easily recognized of all our butterflies. With its wings closed it rather resembles a black dead leaf. It appears in early spring and then again in late summer.

*I-Spy for 5.*

## Painted Lady

This lovely butterfly arrives from warmer parts of Europe in late spring and lays its eggs on thistles. It often comes into gardens to feed on buddleia flowers, but it also feeds on other flowers such as thistles, knapweeds, and teasels.

*I-Spy for 15*

**Red Admiral**
The distinctive pattern on the wings makes this large butterfly easy to tell from its relatives. In autumn it is very fond of sipping the juice from over-ripe fruits such as fallen apples and plums. The eggs are laid on nettles.
*I-Spy for* **10**

**Comma**
It is obvious how this butterfly gets its name. You can see the white, comma-like marking on the underside of the wing. In this pose it resembles a dead, tattered oak leaf. The upper wings are brownish-orange with black blotches.
*I-Spy for* **20**.

**Pearl-bordered Fritillary**
There are two kinds of Pearl-bordered Fritillaries in Britain: the Large and the Small (pictured). Both kinds are widely spread in woodlands but rather scattered. The Small Pearl-bordered is found in June and July, its larger relative in May and June.
*I-Spy for* **25**

**Marsh Fritillary**
This is our smallest fritillary. Look carefully at the markings; they cannot be confused with those of any other butterfly. It is widely spread in Britain, but always occurs very locally on damp hillsides and in wet woodland rides. The caterpillar feeds on the mauve-flowered devil's-bit scabious.
*I-Spy for* **25**

**Dark Green Fritillary**
One of our largest fritillaries, the upperside is a rich orange-brown with black spots, not unlike the Pearl-bordered. Look out for the green coloration on the underside which is a sure way to identify the Dark Green.
*I-Spy for* **20**

**Meadow Brown**
You will usually see this butterfly sitting with its wings closed, as here. It is similar to the next species, the Small Heath, but twice as big. Its caterpillar feeds on many kinds of grasses, so it is not surprising that this is probably our commonest butterfly.
*I-Spy for* **5**

**Small Heath**
Only half as big as the rather similar Meadow Brown, the Small Heath mainly occurs on heathlands, moors, and downlands. The caterpillar is green, and also feeds on grasses. This butterfly does not fly very much, but often suns itself among the grasses.
*I-Spy for* **15**

**Grayling**
There are few British insects harder to spot than this butterfly when it is at rest on the ground with its wings closed. It is found mainly on heaths and moors, and less commonly on downlands. The uppersides of the wings are brown and orange though rarely seen because the butterfly always rests like this.
*I-Spy for 25*

**Wall Brown**
Its fondness for basking open-winged on walls gives this butterfly its common name. Be careful not to confuse it with a fritillary, because the markings are rather similar. The wall brown, however, is usually much commoner, occurring in many kinds of places.
*I-Spy for 15*

### Speckled Wood

This butterfly is usually found along woodland rides but, sometimes, it also comes into gardens. It has a very long season, and you can usually rely on seeing one or two right through from late spring to early autumn.

*I-Spy for 10*

### Ringlet

The small, eye-like spots on the undersides of the wings make this butterfly easy to recognize and give it its common name. Although it usually feeds with closed wings, as here, it sometimes opens them for a while, revealing the unusually dark brown of the uppersides.

*I-Spy for 15*

**Gatekeeper**
Sometimes called the Hedge Brown, this butterfly's more usual name of Gatekeeper comes from its habit of basking on gates and fence-posts. It is often very common, but puzzlingly absent from some areas. It is smaller than the Meadow Brown, and much more abundantly marked with orange.
*I-Spy for* **10**

**Marbled White**
Although it resembles a 'white', this boldly patterned butterfly is really another 'brown'. On the wing during July, it is almost restricted to downlands on chalk and limestone, but sometimes it strays into areas of long grass elsewhere.
*I-Spy for* **20**

### Duke of Burgundy

Although it looks like a very small fritillary, this butterfly is unrelated to true fritillaries. In fact, it is the only British member of a family of butterflies found mainly in the tropics. Look for it during May on downlands and grassy woodland rides.

*I-Spy for* **40**

### Large White

Another name for this very common butterfly is the Cabbage White because of the caterpillar's liking for cabbage leaves. It is very unpopular with gardeners. The Small White is similar and is also very common but it is only about half the size.

*I-Spy for* **5**

**Green-veined White**
This butterfly usually sits with its wings shut, so you can easily see the distinct greenish veins on their undersides. It is only half as big as the Large White, and is found mostly in woods and marshy places rather than in gardens.
*I-Spy for 15*

**Orange Tip**
Only the male has the lovely orange wingtips; the female rather resembles a green-veined white. In both sexes of the Orange Tip, however, the undersides of the wings are heavily speckled with dots, giving a greenish, camouflaged appearance. It is on the wing early, from late April to the end of May.
*I-Spy for 10*

11

**Clouded Yellow**
This is a migrant to our shores and appears only irregularly. When it does come, however, it often arrives in some numbers and is seen all over the place feeding on knapweeds and thistles. It is a much darker yellow than the far more common Brimstone.
*I-Spy for* **50**

**Brimstone**
It is only the male, pictured here, which is a bright sulphur-yellow colour; the female is very pale greenish yellow. Both sexes can be easily distinguished from other butterflies by the shape of the wings which are pointed at the top. The green caterpillar feeds on the buckthorn tree.
*I-Spy for* **10**

12

## Purple Hairstreak

Usually found in oakwood rides, this small butterfly is seen only rarely near the ground, where it sometimes basks on leaves or sips nectar from flowers. The wings are marked with purple in both sexes, but more so in the male. This is a female.
*I-Spy for 30*

## Green Hairstreak

Look at the line of white dots on the wings which gives these butterflies their name — it looks as though a hair has been drawn across wet paint. This is the only bright-green butterfly in Britain, but it is brown on top when the wings are open. It is found on heaths and moors, and in open woods, in May and June.
*I-Spy for 30*

## Small Copper

The small copper is reasonably common just about anywhere, and quite often comes into gardens. The small, green, rather slug-like caterpillar feeds on dock leaves.
*I-Spy for 20*

13

**Common Blue**
This is by far the commonest of our 'blue' butterflies. Only the male is this lovely bright blue all over; the female is brown with a very strong tinge of blue.
*I-Spy for* **20**

**Adonis Blue**
This butterfly has become much rarer of late, and is now restricted to short-grass downland in the south of England. See how the wing veins are rather black, unlike those of the Common Blue. The female is plain dark brown.
*I-Spy for* **40**.

### Chalkhill Blue

A paler blue than our other 'blues', this species is found mainly on grassy downland, but over a much wider area of southern and central England than the Adonis Blue. Note the row of dark spots along the margins of the hindwings. The female is brown.

*I-Spy for* **25**

### Small Blue

This is the smallest of our 'blues', although both sexes are basically brown in colour. It is only in the male that the brown is faintly tinged with blue. It prefers warm sunny downland slopes over much of Britain, but it is always very local and occurs in distinct colonies.

*I-Spy for* **25**

### Holly Blue

The blue uppersides are usually visible only when the insect is in flight. When perched, it almost always closes its wings, revealing the silvery, almost plain, undersides marked with just a few small black dots. All other truly blue 'blues' have prettily patterned undersides. This one is common in gardens.

*I-Spy for 15*

### Brown Argus

This is a 'blue' in which both sexes are brown! Note the lovely orange markings on the wings, which serve to distinguish it from the otherwise easily confused females of some of the other 'blues'. It is found on downland in May and June and again in August.

*I-Spy for 25*

**Small Skipper**
Skippers hold their wings differently from any other butterflies. The Small Skipper is quite a bright orange-brown and is very common in grassy places where it feeds on thistles and similar flowers.
*I-Spy for 10*

**Large Skipper**
Apart from size, the best way to tell this from the Small Skipper is to look for the pale wing patches which you can see in the photograph here. The caterpillars of both kinds feed on grass.
*I-Spy for 15*

17

**Dingy Skipper**
Much rarer than the Large or Small Skippers, the Dingy Skipper is found mainly on downland in May and June. Although it is widespread, it is always very localized in occurrence. Why do you think this one is sleeping like this?

*I-Spy for **30***
*Double with answer*

**Grizzled Skipper**
This small speckled skipper is unlike any other British butterfly. Look for it on grassy downland slopes and woodland rides in May and June.
*I-Spy for **30***

**Swallowtail**
The bright colours of the Swallowtail caterpillar are like no other British species. In Britain, it feeds only on Milk Parsley in East Anglia. In Europe it eats other plants of the parsley family, and is more common.
*I-Spy for 50*

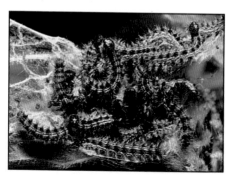

**Small Tortoiseshell**
These spiky caterpillars are usually found in groups on nettles. Look out especially for the yellow lines which help to distinguish it from the Peacock's caterpillars.
*I-Spy for 10*

## Peacock

These caterpillars look generally blacker than those of the Small Tortoiseshell, and are covered with tiny silver spots, lacking any yellow lines. They also feed in groups on nettles. Which is the only bird that regularly eats these spiky caterpil-. lars?

*I-Spy for* **10**
*Double with answer*

## Painted Lady

This big caterpillar lives by itself in a conspicuous silken tent on thistles. Look for it in July and August.
*I-Spy for* **20**

## Large White

Most gardeners are troubled by these caterpillars which are a pest on cabbages and other related vegetables. They usually live in groups because the eggs are laid in clusters

*I-Spy for 10*

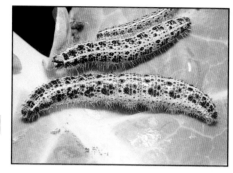

## Butterfly pupa

The pupa of a butterfly or moth is the stage in which the caterpillar changes into an adult. This is the pupa of the Large White butterfly. It is often attached to the woodwork of greenhouses or window-sills. Do you know another special name for a butterfly's pupa?

*I-Spy for 10 — double with answer*

## Moon Moth

Several kinds of giant moon moths with long tails are on show from time to time. They belong to the same family as the British Emperor Moth. The one shown is the American Moon Moth.

*I-Spy for* **25**

## The Flame Butterfly

This lovely orange butterfly has very narrow wings compared with any British species. It comes from the rainforests of South America.

*I-Spy for* **25**

**The Zebra Butterfly**
With its long, narrow wings, it is hardly surprising that this boldly striped butterfly belongs to the same family as the Flame.
*I-Spy for* **25**

**Lacewing Butterfly**
The huge Lacewing butterflies are a common sight in the rainforests of tropical Asia. The black-and-white pattern warns birds to leave them alone because they taste nasty.
*I-Spy for* **25**

**Jezabel Butterfly**
Believe it or not, the colourful Jezabel butterflies belong to the same family as the British Large White butterfly. Jezabels are found in the tropical rainforests of India.
*I-Spy for 25*

**The Malachite Butterfly**
Britain's own little Green Hairstreak butterfly could fit on the wingtips of this big, lime-green butterfly from the South American rainforests.
*I-Spy for 25*

## Common Egg Fly Butterfly

Although it comes from far away Asia and Australia, this butterfly is related to the British Peacock and Small Tortoiseshell butterflies.
*I-Spy for 25*

## Tailed Jay Butterfly

Green is quite a common colour among tropical butterflies, although it is rarely seen in European species. This close relation of the European Swallowtail is found in the rainforests of Asia and New Guinea.
*I-Spy for 25*

## Owl Butterfly

There are many kinds of Owl butterflies from the South American rainforests. They can be easily recognized by the big eye-like markings on the hindwings. The huge caterpillar eats banana leaves.
*I-Spy for 25*

### Five-spot Burnet Moth
Unlike most moths, burnet moths are active in daytime and are brightly coloured. This is a warning to birds to leave them alone because they contain a deadly poison.
*I-Spy for 15*

### Six-spot Burnet Moth
Count the spots! Like the Five-spot Burnet, this moth is usually very abundant wherever it is found and cannot be missed. It particularly likes to feed on the flowers of thistles, knapweed, and scabious.
*I-Spy for 15*

### Transparent Burnet Moth
Instead of the red spots found on other burnets, this species has a large red patch on its wings. In Britain it is restricted to a few mountains in Wales, Scotland, and Ireland, but it is common in Europe.
*I-Spy for 40*

**Forester Moth**
The pretty little green Forester Moths are usually found in May and June on downlands and sunny grassy places. They belong to the same family as the burnet moths.
*I-Spy for 25*

**Cinnabar Moth**
As in the case of the burnets, the bright colours of this moth indicate that it is not good to eat. It is usually found sitting around on yellow-flowered ragwort plants, on which it lays its eggs.
*I-Spy for 15*

### Clearwing Moths
In these moths the wings are partly transparent. Some kinds are striped in black and yellow like wasps. This is the Six-belted Clearwing.
*I-Spy 20 for any clearwing.*
*Double for a Six-belted Clearwing*

### Speckled Yellow Moth
This pretty little moth can be spotted easily by anyone rambling through grassy woodlands or open downlands in May and June.
*I-Spy for 15*

### Hummingbird Hawkmoth
Look for this rather small hawkmoth in your garden during a warm summer. It likes to feed on buddleia and night-scented stocks. It feeds while hovering in front of the flower.
*I-Spy for 30*

**Dusky Sallow Moth**
This moth is active both by day and by night. It feeds on flowers of scabious, knapweed, and thistles. Its caterpillar eats grass.
*I-Spy for 20*

**Common Footman Moth**
Footman moths are rather long and narrow. This is the commonest of them, and can be found feeding on flowers such as ragwort in July and August.
*I-Spy for 15*

## Magpie Moth

If you have goose-berries or currants in your garden, then you will probably have the strikingly patterned Magpie Moth, which prefers to lay its eggs on these bushes. The Magpie is unusual, for most members of its huge family are very drably coloured.

*I-Spy for 20*

## Emperor Moth

This is one of our largest and finest moths. This is a female, which flies at night; the males fly by day. The caterpillar feeds on many different plants.

*I-Spy for 25*

## Convolvulus Hawkmoth

This large grey moth is hard to see when at rest on a fence post. When touched, it opens its wings to display its striped body, which keeps enemies at bay.

*I-Spy for 50*

**Elephant Hawkmoths**

Except for its larger size, the common Elephant Hawkmoth is very similar to the Small Elephant Hawkmoth which is illustrated, and is found mainly on dry downland. The Elephant Hawk often comes into gardens.

*I-Spy for* **25**

**Poplar Hawkmoth**

When at rest, this moth resembles a big dead leaf that is hanging on a tree. Its large caterpillar eats the leaves of poplars and willows.

*I-Spy for* **30**

### Mother Shipton Moth

This and the next nine moths all rest among plants during the day and rather resemble dead fallen leaves. The pattern on the wings is supposed to resemble a scary mask.

*I-Spy for 25*

### Angle Shades Moth

When at rest, this common moth is amazingly like a very shrivelled dead leaf. It usually sits in full view, relying on its camouflage to keep it safe.

*I-Spy for 20*

### Burnished Brass Moth

The resemblance here is more like a partly dead leaf with a tinge of green still present.

*I-Spy for 20*

### Golden Y Moth

In this moth the 'Y' is more of a V plus a golden blob ! It is much prettier than the Silver Y, because it is a more reddish shade of brown.

*I-Spy for 25*

### Golden Plusia Moth

The Golden Plusia often comes to lights around houses. This is because the caterpillar feeds on larkspur and monkshood plants, which are found mostly in gardens.

*I-Spy for 20*

### Silver Y Moth

See how this moth has chosen to rest on a dead leaf so that it is very difficult to spot. This is a common habit. The Silver Y often feeds on garden flowers in August, and is active by day and by night.

*I-Spy for 20*

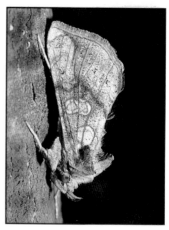

# MOTHS WHICH REST BY DAY

### Herald Moth
You may come across this moth during the winter when it hibernates in an outhouse or greenhouse.
*I-Spy for* **15**

### The Shaded Broad-bar Moth
You should look for this moth in shady, grassy places in July and August. It often sits low down on nettle leaves. This and the Brimstone Moth both have 'looper' caterpillars.
*I-Spy for* **20**

### Brimstone Moth
This moth looks like a yellow, dying leaf. Do you know how this moth and the Brimstone Butterfly got their names?

*I-Spy for* **15**
*Double with answer*

## Pale Prominent Moth

You are most likely to see this moth
when it comes to a lighted window,
as it often does. In Prominent Moths,
a tuft on the forewings sticks up
above the back when the wings are
closed as you can see
from the photograph.
*I-Spy 10 for any prominent moth*
*Double for the Pale Prominent*

## Gold Swift Moth

Swift Moth caterpillars feed on the
roots of plants — in this case, on
those of bracken. The male, shown
here, smells of pineapple.
*I-Spy for 30*

## Common Heath Moth

This moth is found on
almost every heath in
the British Isles. The
adult flies in May and
June, and the
caterpillars feed
mostly on
heathers.
*I-Spy for 25*

### Light Emerald Moth
A fresh specimen of this very common moth is tinged with pale green, but it soon fades to almost white. It is found mostly in woodlands but it is also common in gardens and at lights.
*I-Spy for 10*

### White Ermine Moth
The hairy caterpillar of this common moth eats many kinds of garden plants, so it is not surprising that the adult often comes to lights around houses. During the day it rests on leaves, fences, and so on.
*I-Spy for 15*

### Buff-tip Moth
When at rest, this moth is said to resemble a broken twig, with the yellow patch at the tips of the wings mimicking the freshly broken wood.
*I-Spy for 20*.

**Merveille du Jour Moth**
This lovely moth resembles lichen
growing on a tree trunk. It often
comes into gardens — this one is
resting on an
apple tree.
*I-Spy for 20*

**The Green Pug Moth**
Despite its good camouflage, this
moth was spotted by day sitting on
an apple tree in a garden. Apple is
a favourite foodplant for
the caterpillar.
*I-Spy for 25*

**Mottled Beauty Moth**
This is one of the
easiest moths to find
on tree bark. It is very
common and the
caterpillar eats a wide
variety of
plants.
*I-Spy for 15*

### Common Carpet Moth

If you walk through dampish areas of nettles and brambles in May, you will probably spot this moth. Carpet Moths have 'looper' caterpillars.

*I-Spy for 20*

### Silver-ground Carpet Moth

This carpet moth is found in similar places to the Common species. The wing band is brown rather than blackish. Carpet moths are named for their intricate, carpet-like patterns.

*I-Spy for 20*

### Clouded Border Moth

This moth is very like a splodgy bird dropping. It rests in very damp, shady spots, often under willows, the caterpillar's foodplant.

*I-Spy for 25*

### Yellow-tail Moth

See how this white moth sticks its yellow tail (armed with a tuft of unpleasant, irritating hairs) up through its wings when disturbed, hence its name. It often comes to lights in houses.

*I-Spy for 15*

## Long-horned Moth
There are several kinds of tiny moths in which the males have particularly long antennae ('feelers'). They are usually found in woodlands.
*I-Spy for **20***

## Micro-moth
There are many hundreds of so-called 'micro-' moths less than 1 centimetre long. This tiny species is common on buttercups, and it uses its chewing mouthparts to eat the pollen.
*I-Spy for **20***

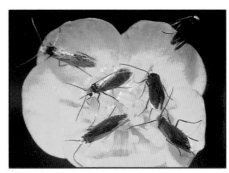

## Plume Moth
Plume Moths are easily recognized by their narrow wings which stick out at their sides like those of an aircraft. They often come to lights around houses.
*I-Spy for **10***

## Buff-tip Moth
These spectacular caterpillars are more often seen than the adult, as they are common on fruit trees in gardens. They always feed in groups. Look out for them in late summer and early autumn.
*I-Spy for 10*

## Garden Tiger Moth
This 'woolly bear' caterpillar eats many different plants, including those in gardens. In autumn, you may see them hurrying across a pavement in search of somewhere to pupate.
*I-Spy for 10*

**Lackey Moth**
Fruit trees in gardens are a favourite food for this caterpillar. This is a fully grown specimen. When smaller, they live in conspicuous groups on silken webs. The adult moth is dull brown.
*I-Spy for 10*

**Drinker Moth**
This is one of the largest of our hairy caterpillars. It is found mostly during May in rather damp places, such as marshes and riversides. The adult is light brown in colour.
*I-Spy for 20*

**Grey Dagger Moth**
Look out for the grey, dagger-like spike on this caterpillar's back. It feeds on many different trees — this one was on an ornamental whitebeam in a garden.
*I-Spy for 20*

## Yellow-tail Moth

May and June are the months to look out for this lovely caterpillar, mainly on hawthorns, apple, and rose. Never touch a hairy caterpillar — especially not this one — because it may cause a nasty irritation.

*I-Spy for 20*

## Vapourer Moth

The amazing brush-like tufts along the back of this lovely caterpillar are typical of its family, the tussock moths. It feeds on almost any kind of plant in summer. The brown female is wingless.

*I-Spy for 15*

## Pale Tussock Moth

The caterpillar can be either green or yellow. It eats many different plants, including hops — hence one of its other common names, the 'hop dog'. The adult moth is pale grey.

*I-Spy for 25*

## Burnet Moth

The rather stubby black-and-yellow caterpillars of the burnet moths are easy to spot — especially after one has climbed up a grass stem to spin its cocoon, as shown in the photograph.

*I-Spy for 15*
*Double if spinning cocoon*

**Cinnabar Moth**
Although it looks smooth, there are a few hairs here and there. It feeds in groups on yellow-flowered ragwort plants. The bright colours warn birds that the caterpillar tastes nasty.
*I-Spy for 10*

**Magpie Moth**
Gooseberry and blackcurrant leaves are this caterpillar's favourite food.
*I-Spy for 15*

**Elephant Hawkmoth**
Some people think they have spotted a small snake when they spy this huge caterpillar with its eye-like markings. It feeds mainly on willowherb, but also sometimes on certain garden plants.
*I-Spy for 25*

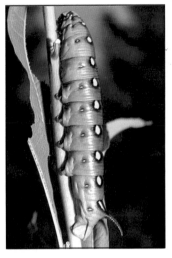

### Bedstraw Hawkmoth
Notice the curved 'tail' which is a characteristic feature of most hawkmoth caterpillars. It feeds on bedstraws and willowherb, especially on coastal sand dunes. Rare in Britain, it is much more common in Europe.
*I-Spy for 50*

### Pebble Prominent Moth
The zig-zag shape of this caterpillar is quite characteristic. It feeds on willows in autumn, and is common in woodlands. The adult is brownish in colour.
*I-Spy for 20*

### Figure-of-eight Moth
The name is derived from marks, similar to the numeral 8, which appear on the adult's forewings. The caterpillar is common on fruit trees from April to June.
*I-Spy for 20*

**Broom Moth**
This handsome caterpillar's basic ground colour can be either green or brown. It eats many different kinds of plants and can be seen in August and September, sitting around quite conspicuously.
*I-Spy for 25*

**Mullein Moth**
Hairy-leaved mulleins or smooth-leaved figworts are the foodplants of this colourful caterpillar. The adult moth is a disappointingly drab brown.
*I-Spy for 20*

**Stick Caterpillar**
There are many kinds of stick caterpillars, all of which move forwards using a looping action, so they are also called 'loopers'. This particular caterpillar is a Peppered Moth.
*I-Spy for 15*

# INDEX

---

## Answers

Small Tortoiseshell: to hibernate. Dingy Skipper: it is well camouflaged on the brown dead seedhead. Peacock: the cuckoo. Butterfly's pupa: a chrysalis. Brimstone Moth: they are the same shade of yellow as brimstone, which is the name for sulphur.

---

ISBN (paperback) 1 85671 128 5

Michelin Tyre Public Limited Company
Davy House, Lyon Road, Harrow, Middlesex HA1 2DQ

MICHELIN and the Michelin Man are Registered Trademarks of Michelin

Edited and designed by Curtis Garratt Limited, The Old Vicarage, Horton cum Studley, Oxford OX9 1BT

The Publisher gratefully acknowledges the contribution of Premaphotos Wildlife who provided all the photographs in this I-Spy book. The Publisher also wishes to acknowledge Ken Preston-Mafham who wrote the text.

Colour reproduction by Anglia Colour Limited.

Printed in Spain.